On the cover is a field ion microscope view of the arrangement of atoms in a crystal, which has a diameter of four millionths (0.000004) of an inch. Each tiny white dot is a single atom, and each ring system is a crystal facet or plane. Dr. Erwin W. Mueller, inventor of this microscope, took the photograph.

The Understanding the Atom Series

Nuclear energy is playing a vital role in the life of every man, woman, and child in the United States today. In the years ahead it will affect increasingly all the peoples of the earth. It is essential that all Americans gain an understanding of this vital force if they are to discharge thoughtfully their responsibilities as citizens and if they are to realize fully the myriad benefits that nuclear energy offers them.

The United States Atomic Energy Commission provides this booklet to help you achieve such understanding.

Edward J. Brunenkant

Edward J. Brunenkant, Director
Division of Technical Information

ATOMIC
PARTICLE
DETECTION

By Hal Hellman

CONTENTS

United States Atomic Energy Commission
Division of Technical Information
Library of Congress Catalog Card Number: 70-606754
1970

ATOMIC PARTICLE DETECTION

by Hal Hellman

INTRODUCTION

Man's eyes are penetrating, keen, and versatile, but there is much he cannot see. So, clever creature that he is, he has developed instruments to extend his vision.

About 350 years ago he invented the telescope and the microscope. The first revealed many secrets of the large-scale universe—the parts of our solar system, the vastness of space, the fantastic multitude and variety of heavenly objects.

The microscope was, in a sense, an even more important invention, for it was a window on a world man never even suspected. In 1675 Anton van Leeuwenhoek, the Dutch biologist and microscopist, wrote of seeing little animals 10,000 times smaller than the water flea, which is a creature that can just barely be seen with the naked eye. By revealing the existence of these organisms, which he called "the most wretched creatures I have ever seen", he put us on the track of scientific farming, improved sanitation, the study of cells, true causes of diseases, and much else.

Just over 200 years later, a number of scientists concluded, from both theoretical and experimental work, that atoms were the basic unit of matter (although no one had ever seen one).

But the problem was, and is, that we cannot see an atom with visible light. We cannot put an atom on the stage of an optical microscope and look at it as we can a water flea or a grain of sand.

But the path of a moving atom, or one of its constituent particles, can be observed and even photographed just as we can observe and photograph a meteor's trail. The particle may also signal its arrival by triggering an electronic or other type of counter. If we could get close enough to a meteor we could see it. Why can't we do the same with atoms?

One reason is that the particles that comprise an atom are constantly in motion. But more important, the wavelength of the light by which we normally see is larger than the size of the particles in which we are interested. It is a little like trying to measure the thickness of a fine wire using an everyday ruler.

An optical microscope cannot distinguish between two things separated by a space less than about 10^{-5} centimeter apart. In technical terms, the resolving power* of the instrument is 10^{-5} cm. This is a small distance, but still a thousand times larger than the size of an atom.

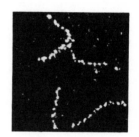

Chains of thorium atoms, magnified 1,000,000 times, in the University of Chicago's scanning electron microscope, which was developed by Dr. Albert V. Crewe and two of his graduate students, Joseph Wall and John Langmore. This is the first time that a closeup view of a single atom has been achieved.

A major step was taken with the development of the electron microscope in the 1930s. In this instrument, a beam of electrons, focussed by an electron lens, produces an enlarged image of a minute object. This is similar to the way in which light is used to form an image in a compound microscope. The electron microscope reveals objects as small as 6×10^{-8} cm., or 6 angstroms.† But the spacing between atoms in a solid is about 3 angstroms!

*The resolving power is the ability of an optical system to form distinguishable images of objects separated by tiny distances.

†An angstrom is equal to the one-hundred-millionth part of a centimeter (10^{-8} cm.).

What might be called the ultimate in microscopes is the recently developed field ion microscope, which can actually produce an image of a single atom on photographic film. While the field ion microscope provides much valuable information on the arrangement of atoms and molecules in various substances, it is still limited to viewing the atom as a whole.

In order to "see" the atom's nucleus and its constituents we need different techniques of observation. What we have said about the combination of visible light and the eye for observing the atom is even more significant in the nuclear domain: The nucleus is 10,000 times smaller in diameter than the atom. Since we cannot see them we must study their effects.

For example, the nuclei of radioactive materials emit radiation—both particles and electromagnetic radiation—that we can study. In the case of nonradioactive substances, we bombard the nuclei with such radiation and observe what "comes out".

In this booklet we are interested in *how* scientists observe the particles that emerge from the nucleus. (From now on when we use the term particles it will mean both particles *and* electromagnetic radiation.) The equipment used falls into two general categories: Counters, which count each particle as it passes by, and track detectors, which make a photographic record of the particle's track.

COUNTERS

Since we cannot see a moving subatomic particle it must "do" something before we know it is there. In the counter method of detection, the particle impinges on a sensitive volume or area, and the detector registers this information. By counting up the number of hits per unit of time we have some indication of the density of the particles involved. Thus counters are very useful as safety devices, because they can warn us that an area or object is dangerously radioactive, i.e., emitting more radiation than is safe for living things.

Counters, however, cannot tell us very much about the position of a particle, except that it struck somewhere within the counter's sensitive volume. On the other hand counters give incredibly good *time resolution**—they can tell when a particle has arrived at a counter to an accuracy of better than 10^{-9} second (a billionth of a second). Some track detectors also have exceptionally good time resolution for sequences of events occurring completely within the device.

Ionization Chambers

When a charged subatomic particle, such as an *electron, proton,* or *alpha particle*† passes through a gas, the electromagnetic field carried along with it rips some of the loosely bound outer electrons from the gaseous atoms. The part of the atom that is left is positively charged and is called a positive *ion.*‡ Although a few of the freed electrons might attach themselves to other atoms or molecules, creating negative ions, most will remain unattached for a while.

---

*Time resolution is the capability of distinguishing between two events that take place at almost the same time; for example events occurring at nearly the same time in a nuclear radiation detector.

†An alpha particle is a positively charged particle emitted by certain radioactive materials. It is made up of two neutrons and two protons bound together and is identical with the nucleus of a helium atom.

‡An ion is an atom or molecule that has lost or gained one or more electrons. By this ionization it becomes electrically charged. Examples: An alpha particle, which is a helium atom minus two electrons; a proton, which is a hydrogen atom minus its electron.

Thus the normal result of the passage of a charged particle through a gas is the production of ion pairs consisting primarily of positive ions and negative electrons.

Electroscopes

The gas—originally neutral and nonconducting—can now conduct electricity.

The first detector to take advantage of this capability was the *electroscope.* Although usually not used to count individual particle hits—it is worth describing because it is the forerunner of an important class of instruments and is still used for certain purposes today. (It was also used in the discovery of cosmic rays in 1911 and 1912.)

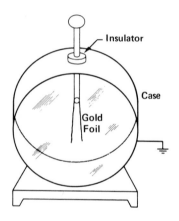

An electroscope.

The basic instrument is shown in the figure. Within a closed volume of air two thin gold leaves hang from a rod that passes through, but is insulated from, the case. The case is normally grounded.

The electroscope is often used for demonstrating experiments in static electricity. When the knob at the top is charged either negatively (excess electrons) or positively, the leaves diverge because the same charge covers both leaves, and like charges repel. The amount of divergence of the leaves is an indication of the amount of charge.

Let us assume that the electroscope is positively charged. If ionizing radiation produces ion pairs in the device, then negative ions (electrons) will drift toward the leaves, combine with some of the excess positive charge, and thereby neutralize the charge. The positive ions will drift toward the case and go down to ground. A sufficient number of such events will cause the leaves to collapse, showing that the charge has been neutralized. The rate at which the foil leaves come together is a measure of the amount of ionizing radiation present. A scale can be added behind the leaves to provide a more quantitative measurement. The device is then called an *electrometer.*

The electroscope does not give any indication of the makeup of the ionizing radiation. Is it alpha particles, beta particles,* or gamma rays?†

Naturally if the experimenter knows that there is only one kind of radiation present and is only interested in determining the amount, then the electroscope alone might do the job. When the radiations are mixed, however, additional steps must be taken. Suppose, for instance, we have a radioactive sample that is emitting all three types of radiation. We can selectively block the various rays since each type has a different penetrating power. Suppose, for example, we put a sheet of paper between the sample and the electroscope. The rate of ionization—as shown by the movement of the gold foil—will slow down. The amount of decrease is an indication of the percentage of the total ionization contributed by the alpha particles.

If we then interpose a sheet of brass, a sixteenth of an inch thick, all the beta particles will also be stopped, and we will know that we have gamma radiation only. More accurate experiments can be made by varying the thickness of these barriers and making additional measurements. In this way it is possible to obtain the absorption curves of the radiations emitted from the sample. An amazing amount of information was obtained from radioactive materials in this manner.

---

*A beta particle is an elementary particle emitted from a nucleus during radioactive decay. A negatively charged beta particle is identical with an electron.

†Gamma rays are high-energy short-wavelength electromagnetic radiation.

Geiger Counters

Although the electroscope is simple and reliable, it has only limited sensitivity. Therefore it has given way to a family of detection instruments that can detect single atomic events. The best known of these is the Geiger—Müller counter. This device is usually called a *Geiger counter*.

The counter was developed by Hans Geiger and W. Müller, one of his students, in 1929, and has become one of the most widely used experimental devices of the 20th century. However, the basic principle was developed about 20 years earlier by Geiger.

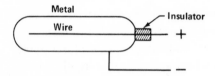

A Geiger counter.

As shown in the figure, the Geiger counter has some similarity to the electroscope, but also varies in a number of important ways. One difference is the existence of a thin wire rather than a foil and rod. Another difference, and the one that made the instrument much more sensitive, was the application of a potential difference between wire and case. The voltage is adjusted in such a way that it is almost ready to discharge through the intervening gas in the chamber.

In other words, as with a number of other detection devices, the tube is then in an unstable (or metastable) condition and is ready to be triggered by a small event. When one or more ionizing particles enters the sensitive volume (see figure on next page) it produces an avalanche of ion pairs. These provide a momentary flow of current, indicating a "hit". Leftover ions are then cleared by some means* so as not to start a new "avalanche", and the device is ready for another count.

Adjustment of the voltage permits the device, when used with additional electronic equipment, to discriminate between, let's say, alpha and beta particles. When used in this

---

*Methods generally used are a reverse voltage pulse and a quenching vapor.

way, the device is called a ***proportional counter*** because the pulses, whose height (or strength) can be measured, are proportional to the rate at which the ionizing radiation loses energy. This rate is higher for slower particles; and for a given energy, the alpha radiation is much slower than the beta because it is much heavier. (In general, all the alpha particles from any radioactive element travel at roughly the same speed.) Thus the alpha will give a stronger pulse and can be distinguished from beta particles.

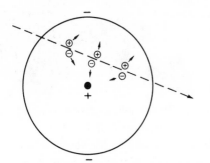

Cross section of a Geiger counter shows how a charged particle creates ion pairs as it passes through.

At a higher potential, the device cannot discriminate between particles but is extremely sensitive. That is, the pulses are all alike but very large. This means that the different particles can't be distinguished by means of the size (shape) of the pulse. The device is then operating as a typical Geiger counter. The resulting pulse may be connected to a device that makes a click for every hit, or it can be connected to a visual counter. In either case the result is a generalized radiation detector that is widely used in schools, industries, hospitals, scientific laboratories, and in prospecting for radioactive minerals.*

In current instruments the ionization current is detected electronically. In the early ionization chambers the current flow was measured with an electrometer. With this simple combination the great British physicist Ernest Rutherford, working with Geiger, showed in 1908 that alpha particles are

---

*See ***Sources of Nuclear Fuel,*** another booklet in this series.

doubly ionized (charged) helium atoms. This was an important experiment, for if alpha particles were to be useful as "atomic probes", it was important that their nature be well understood.

Two of many uses of Geiger counters. On the right a counter measures the number of gamma rays given off by radioactive iodine-131 in the patient's thyroid gland. This information is used to diagnose disorders of the thyroid. On the left a prospector uses a Geiger counter to detect radioactive uranium in the earth.

Scintillation Counters

The modern Geiger counter, although widely used, and capable of "seeing" single atomic particles, does have disadvantages. One is its inability to measure energy. Most serious is the fact that it takes a certain amount of time for the equipment to readjust to normal, or "recompose" itself, after it has registered a count. Although modern equipment can bring this *dead time* down to only 100 *millionths* of a second, this is long enough to introduce large errors into some experiments.

Another major class of instrument, the *scintillation counter,* gets around this problem by tapping the energy of an energetic nuclear particle in a different way. Many substances have the ability to convert the kinetic energy of a moving particle into visible light. Such a material is called a phosphor, or scintillator. For example, if an alpha particle falls onto a screen coated with zinc sulphide, it produces a tiny light flash that is bright enough to be seen in the dark with the aid of a magnifying lens or microscope.

In one of the most famous experiments of all time, suggested by Rutherford and performed in his laboratory, this simple detector was used in the discovery of the atomic nucleus. The experimental setup is shown in the figure. As shown in (a), a small amount of alpha particle scattering was expected when they were passed through a thin gold foil. It was found, however, that some of the particles bounced back at large angles.

As Rutherford put it, this was "almost as if you fired a 15-inch shell at a piece of tissue paper, and it came back and hit you". He reasoned, in his famous paper of 1911, that this could only be explained by the presence of a positively charged, tiny nucleus at the center of each atom.

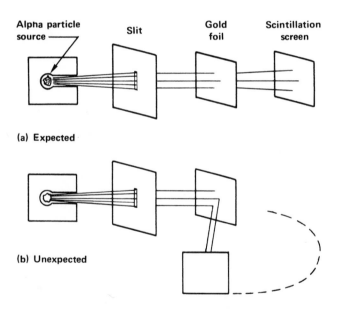

Use of scintillation detector in the discovery of the atomic nucleus.

This great success notwithstanding, the scintillator method was slow, tiring, and not completely reliable. It has been said that whenever Rutherford himself did the actual counting, he would "damn" vigorously for a few minutes and then have one of his assistants take over. Before they were finished, the experimenters had counted over a million scintillations (flashes).

One of these assistants was Hans Geiger! Perhaps then it is no coincidence that Geiger was to be the one who developed a method of detecting nuclear particles that would release the human counter from his work.

With the development of ionization counters, the scintillation method went into decline. Except for some use in school laboratories, it was obsolete for about 20 years.

Its resurrection coincided with the development of television. The combination of electron beam and phosphors used in a television tube has been applied in a special type of electronic tube called a *photomultiplier.* This device exceeds the sensitivity of the human eye. A photomultiplier tube converts the light output of the scintillator into an electric pulse that can be counted automatically.

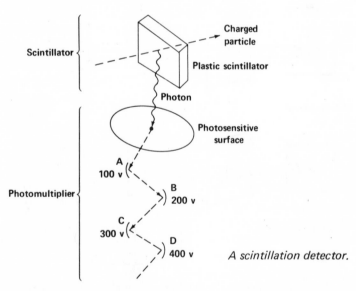

A scintillation detector.

The principle of operation is shown in the figure. A charged particle passing through the scintillator causes a number of photons of light to be emitted. When a photon strikes the photosensitive surface of the photomultiplier tube, it causes the ejection of an electron that is attracted to electrode A by a potential difference of 100 volts. This potential difference causes acceleration of the electron until additional electrons are knocked out of the electrode. The process is repeated. In this way a few photons can lead to the production of a large number of electrons from the final electrode. The signal can be further amplified.

The scintillation method provides other advantages, such as short pulse duration and short recovery time. Also a wide variety of materials—gaseous, liquid, or solid—can be used as the scintillation medium, and this permits many different applications for the system.

The original zinc sulphide screen used by Rutherford was opaque, and so anything that happened inside the material was lost. This is why the device was most useful with alpha particles; because alphas are readily stopped, the interactions took place at the surface of the material. Betas and gammas, with greater penetrating power, could therefore not be "seen" in this way. A great step was taken when it was learned that transparent materials could also be used as scintillators. Then actions taking place *inside* the material

A technician examines a new light detector that can seek out flashes of light too weak or too brief to be detected by the human eye. The device uses an amplifying section made of gallium phosphide that is 10 times more efficient than those presently in use. The tube may be used to detect light from mysterious radio stars called pulsars, to see more deeply into the structure of atoms, to learn how green plants convert sunlight into food, and to further decipher the chemical code of life.

could also be counted, and scintillators could be used to detect betas and gammas as well as alphas.

A typical scintillation counter consists of the scintillating material and a photomultiplier tube. Sometimes they are combined into one instrument as shown on page 11. In other applications, perhaps because of the geometry of the experiment, it might be necessary to separate the two devices. In such case a "light tube" (or "light pipe") is used. This material can be bent optically in various ways, and yet will still carry the light flashes from one end to the other without their being lost through the walls of the pipe.

The electrical pulses coming from a scintillation counter can be very short—in some cases as little as a few billionths

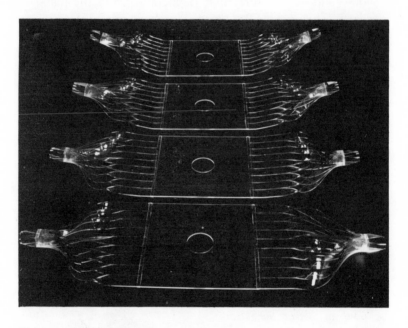

"Light pipes" are used when scintillation detector and photomultiplier tubes are not adjacent or have different configurations.

of a second. Hence there is less of a problem with dead time than in the Geiger counter. In many cases the brightness of the flashes can be measured by the pulse height and these provide valuable information on the energy of the particles or electromagnetic radiation. A special electronic device called a *pulse-height analyzer* has been developed that, when used in conjunction with counters, can provide a great deal of information from gamma-ray emission; it is sensitive even to very feeble sources. The analyzer contains a large number of channels, each of which is only sensitive to pulses of a certain height.

The result is an energy spectrum of radiation that is comparable to the visible spectrum of a light source. As in

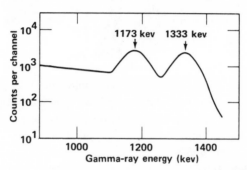

Gamma-ray energy spectrum of radioactive cobalt-60.

visible light spectroscopy,* this spectrum provides information on the material emitting the radiation as well as on the amount present. Gamma-ray energy peaks at 1,173 and 1,333 Kev† tell us that we are dealing with radioactive cobalt-60. The height of the peaks, which is derived from the number of counts per channel, gives an indication of the amount of ^{60}Co present.

Counters with liquid phosphors can be made in a variety of shapes. Two are shown on page 14, including a hollow, cylindrical· *whole body counter* for measuring the total radioactivity of a body.

Another interesting example of a liquid scintillator is the large cylindrical device used by Frederick Reines and Clyde L. Cowan, Jr., to detect the very elusive antineutrino. As shown in the figure, the events were "seen" by 90

---

*See *Spectroscopy,* another booklet in this series.

†KeV stands for kilo electron volts or 1000 electron volts.

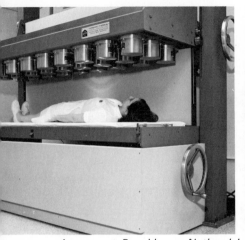
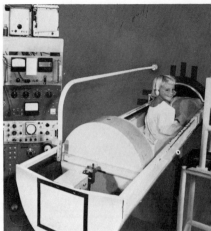

A nurse at Brookhaven National Laboratory in New York simulates a patient in this highly sensitive, whole body, gamma-ray detection system. Fifty-four sodium-iodine crystals are used, half above and half below the patient. On the right is another whole body counter. The patient lies in a bed that slides into a hollow space inside a cylindrical tank of scintillation fluid.

Liquid scintillation detector (cylindrical object at the bottom) used to discover the antineutrino.

photomultiplier tubes spaced around the cylinder. These experiments were conducted in 1953 and 1955–56.*

As we shall see in more detail later, the fields of high-energy and cosmic-ray physics introduce a complication into the detection process: The energies of the particles involved are so high that they have great penetrating power and therefore need large detection volumes. They also tend to create cascades of additional particles. Until recently, scintillation crystals had been too small to absorb all the energy and particles released in a particle reaction.

A new instrument, being developed by Professor Robert Hofstadter, a Stanford University physicist, is expected to be able to measure the energy of the most energetic particles produced in today's largest particle accelerators.† The heart of the new detector is a giant cylindrical crystal of sodium iodide (see figure on page 16). The crystal may be up to 30 inches in diameter and 5 or more feet in length, depending on the kind of particle reactions to be observed. Although "growing" a 5-foot crystal is not yet practicable, several crystal sections can be stacked to obtain the proper length.

Robert Hofstadter.

---

*A neutrino is a neutral elementary particle with a negligible mass that interacts very weakly with matter and therefore is very difficult to detect. Antimatter is matter in which ordinary nuclear particles are replaced by their counterparts: Antiprotons instead of protons, antineutrinos instead of neutrinos, positrons instead of electrons, etc. Normal matter and antimatter would mutually annihilate each other upon contact, being converted totally into energy. See *The Elusive Neutrino,* another booklet in this series.

†See *Accelerators,* another booklet in this series.

Large size crystals make this a total absorption detector that provides high efficiency and usefulness at very high energies.

Because of the material's great density, reactions associated with a single event all take place within a relatively short distance, and this provides a size advantage over liquid scintillators. A major advantage of the crystal detector is that, while larger crystals are needed for higher energies, the size requirement goes up much more slowly than the energy the device can handle.

High-energy particles from an accelerator or other source enter the detector at one end. The energy released causes flashes of bright light. As in a standard scintillation counter, photomultiplier tubes mounted around the crystal measure the brightness and time of occurrence of the flashes; in this way data are provided from which types of particles and reactions can be identified. It is hoped that the device will be able to detect the energy of many particles involved in high-energy physics.

Semiconductor Detectors

Although scintillation and gas detectors are still widely used, they are rapidly being displaced in the field of nuclear spectroscopy by semiconductor detectors. The advantage of these devices is that they can measure the energy of a particle or a *quantum* of radiation very accurately. The improved precision in the energy measurements occurs because the ionizing particle of a given energy produces about 10 times the amount of ionization in a solid as in a gas; thus the effect of electrical noise in the detector and the signal amplifier are proportionately reduced.

However, both the detector and the amplifier produce some electrical noise that may obscure the signal in some way. The primary advantage of the semiconductor detector is its greater precision, i.e., the pulse height measures the energy absorbed with less statistical error. The comparative spectra in the figure show the greater resolution (sharper peaks) of the semiconductor signal.

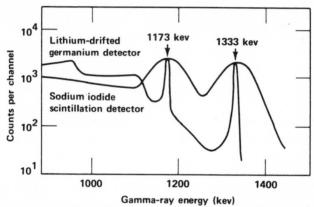

Comparative spectra from scintillation and semiconductor detectors show the superior resolving power of the semiconductor type.

A semiconductor is a solid crystalline material whose electrical conduction properties lie somewhere between that of a conductor (such as metal) and an insulator (such as glass). In a certain sense the semiconductor detector behaves like a gas counter in that ion pairs are formed when the material is exposed to energetic radiation, with a resultant change in the electrical conductivity.

However, in the semiconductor a much smaller energy is necessary to create an ion pair so that a given energy absorbed from the particle will result in many more ion pairs. It is this increase in number of pairs that results in the higher resolution. As in the other types of detectors, the radiation has been made to "do" something. The change in conductivity is monitored by applying a voltage across the device and measuring the change.

Semiconductor detectors consist of a block of very pure single-crystal silicon or germanium. Early detectors of this type, introduced in 1945 by the Dutch scientist P. J. Van Heerden, were made of industrial diamonds, but imperfections in the diamond crystals spoiled their performance. In the 1960s, silicon and germanium crystals, which were developed for transistors, were pure and perfect enough to use for detectors.

Although the major applications so far have been in the field of nuclear physics, the small size and efficiency of these devices have led to applications in biology, medicine, and space research. Counters have been developed that are small enough to be swallowed or even inserted into the body with hypodermic needles for the treatment of disease. These are very useful when used in conjunction with radioactive tracers. By using radioisotopes to tag certain substances, which are taken up in specific ways by the body (e.g., radioactive iodine in the thyroid gland), scientists have been able to study a number of life processes in detail.*

Precise spectroscopy using semiconductor detectors demands rather complex apparatus. For the best results, detectors must be cooled to liquid nitrogen temperature and very refined electronics must be used. Despite this, the tremendous importance in nuclear physics of accurate energy measurements has brought about a spectacular increase in the use of semiconductor detectors.

Čerenkov Counters

In 1934 the Russian physicist Pavel A. Čerenkov (cher-wren-cough) noted that an intense beam of gamma rays directed into water produced a faint bluish-white light. He reported also that the light seemed to be given off in a cone traveling in the same direction as the beam (see figure). And, finally, if the water were replaced with benzene, the angle of the cone increased by a few degrees.

The explanation for this effect, given a few years later by the Russian physicists Ilya M. Frank and Igor Y. Tamm, is

---

*See *Radioisotopes in Medicine* and *Radioisotopes and Life Processes,* other booklets in this series.

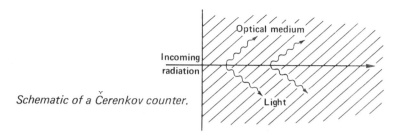

Schematic of a Čerenkov counter.

based on a most unexpected observation: A highly energetic particle can travel faster than light through certain optical media. This does not contradict the theory of relativity, which only states that the maximum velocity of an object cannot exceed the velocity of light in a *vacuum*. The velocity of light through some transparent substances (such as a diamond) can be less than half its speed in a vacuum. In high-energy physics, on the other hand, particles often travel through material substances at speeds approaching the speed of light in a vacuum!

The result of a particle traveling faster than light in an optical medium is a shock wave, very similar to the one produced by a supersonic aircraft that is traveling faster than the speed of sound in air. The cone of light given off is thus analogous to the cone-shaped sonic boom of the aircraft except that they point in opposite directions.

The faster the particle moves through the medium, the larger will be the angle of the cone. This angle, which is easily measured, provides information on the velocity of the particle. By using different media, the experimenter can use the counter as a threshold detector, i.e., one that will record only particles whose velocity exceeds the light velocity in the medium. All those with velocities below that value will be "ignored" simply because they will not produce Čerenkov radiation. While this may sound like a negative kind of advantage, it is a very real asset: One of the major problems in many high-energy physics experiments is a profusion of particles and data. Anything that can cut out unnecessary "verbiage" is appreciated. Vanes or louvers can be used to block off the light emitted by particles with higher velocities than those desired.

Basically the device is operated like a scintillation counter, including photomultiplier tubes. As in scintillation counters, the device is often enclosed in some kind of container whose inner walls are silvered or painted white to reflect as much of the light into the tubes as possible. This is even more important in Čerenkov counters because the light given off is so feeble.*

A Čerenkov counter was used in the identification of the antiproton by Emilio Segrè, Owen Chamberlin, C. Wiegand, and T. Ypsilantis in 1955.† The device used is shown in the figure. In this experiment the antiproton had to be selected out of a beam consisting almost entirely of *pi-mesons*.‡ Because the antiproton—if it existed—was expected to be some 6½ times more massive than the mesons, its speed in a beam of known particle *momentum* would be less and could be calculated because momentum equals mass times velocity. The cone angle could also be calculated and was predicted to exist at about 31° while the faster mesons would produce a cone angle of about 48°.

The smaller cone was indeed found, even though there was only about 1 antiproton for every 40,000 mesons!

Čerenkov detector used in iden-
tification of the antiproton.

---

*Some readers may be puzzled by the fact that Čerenkov saw visible light, since the incident radiation was gamma rays and not particles. What undoubtedly happened was that the gamma rays, which intrinsically are high-energy photons, knocked some electrons loose in the medium, and these caused the visible light that has come to be called Čerenkov radiation.

†Emilio Segre and Owen Chamberlin received the Nobel Prize in 1959 for their discovery.

‡A meson is one of a class of short-lived elementary particles with a mass between that of the electron and that of the proton. The mass of a charged pi-meson is about 273 times that of an electron; that of a neutral pi-meson is 264 times that of an electron.

Time-of-Flight Measurement

Because velocity discrimination was so important in the experiment, Segrè and his co-workers did not depend only on the Čerenkov counters. They also timed the particles during one 40-foot portion of their trip from accelerator to Čerenkov counters. They could do this because of the remarkable time resolution capabilities of scintillation counters. The speed of the particles was measured by comparing the delay between counts in two scintillation detectors, one at the start of the 40 feet and one at the end. For pi-mesons, or pions, the time required was 4×10^{-8} second as compared with 5×10^{-8} second for the anti-protons.

This technique is called *time-of-flight measurement.* It is often used when dealing with neutral particles, since these cannot be separated by magnetic means.

Coincidence Counting

One last counting technique must be mentioned before we go on to discuss track-forming devices. In counters, the larger the device the *less* sure we are of just where the particles struck. In accelerator experiments this may not be a problem because we have quite good control over the beam. We cannot, however, control cosmic-ray bombardment, which assaults the earth from all directions.*

Thus, in some very delicate experiments, where very few counts are involved, a stray hit by a cosmic-ray particle could confuse the results. These rays themselves are being intensively studied largely because we still are not sure how they obtain their incredible energies—energies that are often millions of times higher than anything we can produce even in our largest particle accelerators.

Because counters (except for Čerenkov detectors) do not tell the angle of a particle's path, nor even whether the particle entered from the front, rear, top, or bottom of the counter, another method must be used to give us this

---

*See *Space Radiation* and *The Natural Radiation Environment,* other booklets in this series.

information. (Even simple shielding, i.e., shielding all sides except the desired one, may not work; a strong hit by a cosmic-ray particle on the shield can produce a shower of radiation within the detector.) A technique that has found wide use is *coincidence counting.*

Coincidence counting is a method for detecting or identifying radioactive materials and for calibrating their disintegration rates by counting two or more characteristic radiation events, which occur together or in a specific time relationship to each other.

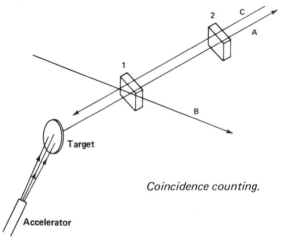

Coincidence counting.

The principle is similar to that of time-of-flight measurement, although of course the objective is quite different. As shown, two or more counters are lined up with their sensitive areas parallel. Although counter 1 cannot tell us from which direction particle B has come, the fact that counter 2 did not register a count at the proper time after counter 1 registered a count tells us that it is an unwanted hit. Particle C presents a slightly more difficult problem. But thanks to the excellent time resolution of these devices we can tell that particle A is going in the right direction while particle C is not. Screening out particles we do not want is called *anticoincidence counting.*

By interposing shielding of various kinds between the counters, we can also select particles by screening out those of lower momentum.

TRACK FORMING DETECTORS

An experienced game hunter can deduce an extraordinary amount of information from a set of tracks. So too can a particle physicist.

The nuclear or high-energy physicist often wants to know more than the fact that a particle has passed through his detector. He may want as complete a "life history" as possible, including the direction of the particle's motion, the length of its path, its mass, charge, energy, and so on. In addition, he will probably want to observe where and how the incoming particle reacts with atoms and/or nuclei in his detector. He will want to examine the new paths taken, and perhaps the new particles that may be produced. A variety of track detection devices have been developed that enable him to do all these things.

Putting the situation another way, we might say that what counters can do by artifice, e.g., coincidence counting, track-forming detectors do automatically.

Cloud Chambers

Ideas for scientific equipment arise in many ways and from many sources. In 1894 Charles T. R. Wilson, the Scots physicist, became fascinated by the play of sunlight on clouds surrounding Ben Nevis, the highest of the Scottish hills. He was particularly intrigued by colored rings that encircled the sun and other rings which surrounded the shadow cast by the hilltop on mist or cloud.

He later wrote that "this greatly excited my interest and made me wish to imitate them in the laboratory. At the beginning of 1895 I made some experiments for this purpose—making clouds by expansion of moist air. . . . Almost immediately I came across something which promised to be of more interest than the optical phenomena I had intended to study."

This "something" gave scientists the *cloud chamber*, which allows them to "see" atomic particle tracks through space. He won a Nobel Prize in physics in 1927 for this invention.

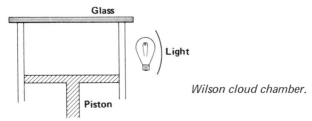

Wilson cloud chamber.

Wilson's cloud chamber is shown schematically in the figure. A glass container fitted with a movable piston is filled with moisture-saturated air. Keeping in mind the fact that air cools when allowed to expand, we pull down the piston. At a certain point the cooling vapor becomes supersaturated, i.e., it carries more moisture than it normally would at that temperature and will try to "unload" the moisture on any available surface. The same phenomenon is seen when moisture condenses on a cold glass in warm weather.

When a charged particle moves through a gas or other matter, the electric field carried along with it knocks electrons out of some of the atoms it encounters. As in the gas-type detectors, the particle thus leaves a trail of charged atoms, or ions, behind it. In the cloud chamber this trail provides convenient points of deposit for the buildup of droplets in the chamber. Thus a foggy line of droplets marks the passage of a charged particle speeding through the chamber.

Ernest Rutherford had this to say about the method:

> To the period 1895–1912 belongs the development of an instrument which to my mind is the most original and wonderful in scientific history. . . . It was a wonderful advance to be able to see, so to speak, the details of the adventures of these particles in their flight through the gas. Anyone with imagination who has seen the beautiful stereoscopic photographs of the trails of swift alpha particles, protons, and electrons cannot but marvel at the perfection of detail with which their short but strenuous lives are recorded.

000 times more dense than gases, chamber size could also ḍuced considerably. However, this is not to say that e chambers are all small. Far from it. Although Glaser's evice was only 3 centimeters long and 1 centimeter in er, later bubble chambers are 80 inches long. A one has been proposed for the giant accelerator being Batavia, Illinois.

mber (left) and the 80-inch, liquid hydrogen bubble en National Laboratory.

vices, given early stimulation by Luis W. ẹcessary with the development of particle e billion-electron-volt range. Dr. Glase ize in Physics in 1960 for his work; i vas similarly honored for his decisiv ḥ-energy physics, among the most i his work on large bubble chambers. erent liquids have been used in mode vy liquids, such as Freon and xenon

The usefulness of cloud chambers was increased by the fact that they could operate under a wide variety of conditions. The chamber size could be varied from 1 to 36 inches in diameter. The nature of the gas could be changed at will and it was possible to operate at gas pressures as high as 100 atmospheres. (One atmosphere equals 14.7 pounds per square inch.) This shortened the trip of the particle or particles and made it more likely that the desired interactions would all take place within the chamber.

Another useful feature was that the trail of ions persisted for a few moments after the particle had passed through. It was therefore possible to operate the chamber in conjunction with a coincidence counter, so that the latter caused a camera to take photos only when it "thought" that an interesting event had taken place.

One of the problems with the Wilson cloud chamber was the long time required for recovery after an expansion. In some cloud chambers it took as long as several minutes to bring the equipment back to a condition of sensitivity with no old tracks remaining. An improvement on the expansion type chamber is the *diffusion cloud chamber*, which operates continuously. Plans for a simple diffusion cloud chamber are given on pages 52-53. However, in research, the cloud chamber has been replaced by other devices.

Identification of Particles

As implied by Rutherford's statement, the cloud chamber enables us to detect, observe, and identify a single particle. This identification is done in a number of interesting ways.

The most important technique involves the use of a magnetic field. When a charged particle—and most of the particles involved in nuclear and high-energy physics are charged—moves through a magnetic field, a force acts upon the particle at right angles to the direction of the field.

As shown in the figure, a negatively charged particle traveling through a magnetic field directed into the paper would curve to the right. A positive particle would curve to the left. An uncharged particle would not curve at all. (Nor, normally, would it even leave a track. We shall see later how

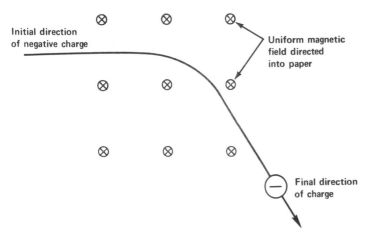

Initial direction
of negative charge

Uniform magnetic
field directed
into paper

Final direction
of charge

A force acts on a charged particle moving through a magnetic field, causing it to travel in a curved path.

the tracks of uncharged particles and gamma rays are detected.) A more massive or a faster moving particle would have a smaller curvature, while the track of a doubly charged particle of the same mass and velocity would be curved twice as much.

This technique was used in the discovery of the positron, the antiparticle of the electron, in 1932. When the American physicist C. D. Anderson examined the photo shown in the figure, he thought the particle track *had* to be that of a positive electron. A negative electron would have curved in the opposite direction while a proton (the only other positively charged particle known at the time) would have had much less curvature.

The bar across the center is a 6-millimeter-thick lead plate, which aided Anderson in deciding on the all-important direction in which the particle is moving (upward). Clearly the particle will be moving more slowly after it passes through the barrier; hence its path after emerging will be more highly curved. The positron was described by Anderson as "one of those rare upward-moving cosmic-ray particles".

Thickness and length of track are other clues used by the observer in determining particle type and/or energy. In-

First picture of the positron was tak[en] the right is C. D. Anderson.

terestingly, the slower the
Why? Sweep a magnet pa
quickly; then slower and
during the fast or slow sw
    Often two pictures
different angles in o
stereoscopic viewing
the placement of the

Bubble Chambers

The **bubble**
detection device
is analogous t
instead of a ga
particles, bei
through a cl
order to inc
in order to
denser me
    The
Donald
interac

*The first bubble cha
chamber at Brookha*

to 10
be re
bubb
first d
diamet
25-foo
built at

These huge de
Alvarez, became n
accelerators in th
received a Nobel P
1968 Dr. Alvarez
contributions to hig
portant of which was
    A number of diff
bubble chambers. Hea

28

liquid form), have been used at least partially because their nuclei, being large, are more likely to be struck by incoming particles than are those of smaller, lighter molecules and atoms. Another reason is that the paths of any radiation products given off are shorter.

However, results are difficult to analyze because of the fact that these substances contain a complicated assemblage of atoms. The chemical formula for heavy Freon, for instance, is CF_3Br. When such a molecule is bombarded and broken apart, it is difficult to figure out what happened.

Thus the most widely used fluid is liquid hydrogen, whose nuclei are protons. A bubble chamber photo illustrating a high-energy interaction between an incoming K-minus and a target proton is shown in the figure, along with an explanation of the interactions. This photo was the first to show the existence of the Omega Minus particle, the existence of which had been predicted by the American physicist Murray Gell-Mann and the Israeli physicist Yuval Ne'eman. (See figure on page 30.)

Operation of a bubble chamber is similar in principle to that of the Wilson cloud chamber, with one significant difference. Pressure in the bubble chamber is initially high, and is then released. The liquid thus becomes superheated, whereas the gas in the cloud chamber becomes supercooled. The result, however, is similar: Bubbles will form along any irregularities in the liquid and also along the ion tracks left by charged particles passing through.

This explains why the bubbles in a pan of water form on the sides and bottom of the pan; irregularities on the metal provide the first "footholds" for vaporization to take place. (It is said that Glaser got his idea for the bubble chamber while watching bubbles form in a glass of beer.)

In modern bubble chambers the bubble tracks are photographed by several stereo cameras. This permits the event to be reconstructed no matter what orientation is involved or how complicated the interaction.

Another similarity with cloud chambers is the widespread use of magnetic fields to help in unravelling the events. But as can be imagined, huge amounts of power are required to

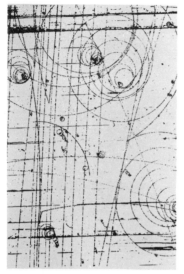
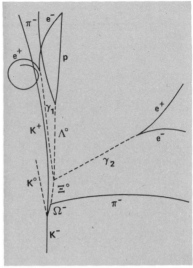

The Omega Minus particle appears for the first time in this bubble chamber picture. This particle is significant because it is the keystone to an orderly arrangement of previously known particles. Photo at left was taken in the 80-inch bubble chamber at Brookhaven. The drawing at the right is a reconstruction of the important tracks. The paths of charged particles are drawn as solid lines, while the paths of neutral particles and electromagnetic radiation (gamma rays), which leave no tracks in the chamber, are shown by broken lines. Note too that they are not curved.

Here is what happened. A negative K-meson (K⁻) enters the bubble chamber from the bottom and collides with a stationary (and hence unseen) target proton (hydrogen nucleus). This collision produces a neutral K-meson (K⁰), a positive K-meson (curving up and to the left), and a negative Omega meson (Ω⁻). This Omega Minus in turn decays (in one ten-billionth of a second) into a negative pi-meson (π⁻) and a neutral cascade hyperon (Ξ⁰). The cascade hyperon leaves no track but can be identified by its decay products: A neutral lambda hyperon (Λ⁰) and two gamma rays (γ₁ and γ₂), each of which decays into electron–positron pairs (e⁻ and e⁺). The neutral lambda in turn yields a negative pi-meson and a proton (p). Knowledge of masses, momenta, and conservation laws enable physicists to identify particles that yield neither tracks nor decay products such as the K⁰ at the lower left.

produce a high, uniform, magnetic field across the large chambers that have been, and will be, built. The problem of removing the heat generated by this power is a serious one. As a result there has been considerable interest in the use of superconducting magnets. At very low temperatures (which are necessary to keep some of the gases in liquid form anyway), certain metals lose *all* their resistance to electricity. They are then called superconductors. Once a current has been started in a superconductor, it continues to circulate even after the power has been shut off.

Another advantage of superconductivity is the production of stronger magnetic fields. Stronger fields cause the particles to curve sharply. As a result particles of higher energies can be measured, and it is easier to discriminate between particles that would otherwise have similar paths.

The world's largest superconducting magnet being installed in a new 148-inch bubble chamber at Argonne National Laboratory in Illinois.

As in the Wilson cloud chamber, the bubble chamber is not continuously sensitive and must be cycled. When the bubble chamber is used with a particle accelerator this is normally not a problem, since the accelerator generally produces bursts of particles at known times. The operation of the two devices is simply synchronized; the timing is arranged so that the particle burst enters the chamber near the time the pressure is at a minimum. This time is varied to achieve certain track properties. Approximately a millisecond later, photographs are taken with the aid of a powerful flash of light. The film is then advanced, and the whole operation is repeated a second or two later.

To obtain a higher speed of operation, which would be useful in some applications, a different method is needed. A new approach in bubble chambers is the use of ultrasonics rather than compression and superheating to make the liquid medium sensitive to incoming particles. This technique is under development at CERN, the European Organization for Nuclear Research in Geneva, Switzerland. Successful operation—including continuous sensitivity!—has already been achieved with liquid helium cooled down to 3.5° K (−269.66°C).

The bubble chamber has been an indispensable tool in the field of high-energy physics. The combination of accelerator and bubble chamber has been a particularly good one; it has added much to our knowledge of particles, fields, forces, and the makeup of the nucleus—and even some inkling of the makeup of subnuclear particles. Indeed it has given scientists the wherewithal to probe the very heart of matter.*

Spark Chambers

Notwithstanding the admitted advantages of the bubble chamber, it has a serious drawback for certain kinds of experiments: Everything that happens during its sensitive interval of about 3×10^{-3} second is indiscriminately photographed.

Thus there are two general types of experiment where the bubble chamber may not be useful. One is the type in which a great profusion of events takes place quickly and in a small space. Here a detection method utilizing a kind of film called nuclear photographic emulsion has generally been used. We discuss this method later on.

---

*For more information, see *Microstructure of Matter* another booklet in this series, or *High Energy Physics,* H. Hellman, J. B. Lippincott Company, 1968.

The other type of experiment is that in which very few events take place over a long period of time. Indeed it sometimes happens that the rarer the event, the more valuable it is.

Columbia University's 10-ton aluminum spark chamber, installed at Brookhaven National Laboratory, showed the existence of two kinds of neutrino.

In 1962, for example, an experiment was conducted which showed that there were two separate and distinct types of neutrino. The experiment lasted for 6 months. During that time the number of recorded events caused by neutrinos averaged out to less than one every 3 days. In a bubble chamber vast numbers of photos would have been taken, most of which would have been useless. But using the more recently developed spark chamber, it was possible to "instruct" the apparatus (by using anticoincidence counters) to take photos only when an event was thought to be of interest. This occurred only a few times a day, at which point a photo was taken by automatic cameras. The photos were later scanned.

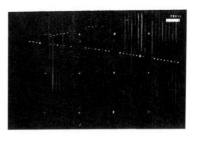

Spark chamber photograph taken during the two-neutrino experiment. Lower track is that of a mu-meson created by an incident neutrino. Upper track is believed to be that of a stray gamma ray.

The spark chamber provides a sort of compromise between the good time resolution of the scintillation counter and the space resolution of the bubble chamber. As shown in the figure, a set of tracks is indeed photographed, but because there are "dead spaces" between the sensitive areas, the path of the particle is not as clearly defined as in the bubble chamber. As a result it cannot be measured with the same accuracy as in a bubble chamber photograph. It is even possible that some aspect of the event might be lost or confused: In the photo the upper track might have branched off from the lower one.

On the other hand, the event can be located in time much more accurately; the spark chamber has a sensitive time of only about a millionth of a second. This very good time resolution, which is the main advantage that the spark chamber has over the bubble chamber, makes it possible to use a much higher particle flux (more particles per second in the bombarding beam) so that the rate of events can be increased many fold. It thus becomes possible to selectively photograph an individual event that is produced by one particular particle among many—indeed among particles that may be passing through at a rate as high as a million a second.

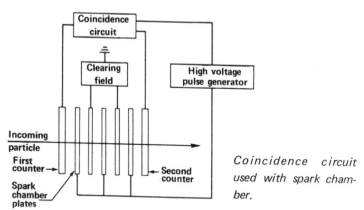

Coincidence circuit used with spark chamber.

This is done by means of an arrangement of coincidence counters, and a *logic circuit.* An example of such a circuit is shown in the figure. Only when the proper set of pulses is produced in the circuit will the camera operate. (Note that the "decision" to photograph is taken after the particle passes through the second counter.) Within about a fiftieth of a second, the film is changed, the chamber is cleared of ions, and the device is ready to record another event. The figures

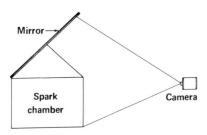

Use of mirror above spark chamber permits camera at Brookhaven to photograph both side and top views with a single shot.

show how use of mirrors above the chambers permits both side and top views to be taken on a single negative.

The spark chamber makes use of the track of ions left in a gas by a charged particle. This path of ions will conduct electricity better than the surrounding gas and, as a result, a spark jumps between adjacent, oppositely charged, plates. The particle thus leaves in its wake a series of sparks between the many plates of the spark chamber. Each spark does not lie along the path of the particle, but rather is horizontal. This adds to the uncertainty of the path.

As with cloud and bubble chambers, a magnetic field is sometimes used to help determine the characteristics of the particles passing through. It is also possible to vary the material, thickness, number, and spacing of the plates to serve the special requirements of the experiment. Variations on the spark chamber—the streamer spark chamber and the wire chamber—provide yet other capabilities.

(A)

(B)

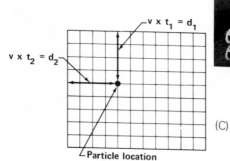

(C)

Locating the coordinates of a particle "hit" in a wire spark chamber

(A) The streamer spark chamber has no plates and hence no breaks in the particle track. (B) "Winding" the wire planes for a sparkostrictive wire chamber. (C) Locating the coordinates of a particle "hit" in a wire spark chamber.

A streamer chamber is shown in (A) above. It is a transparent, plastic insulating box that is filled with helium and a small amount of alcohol vapor. An extremely short high-voltage pulse is passed between electrodes that are placed outside the box. This creates discharges—called streamers—that develop rapidly all along a particle's path in the chamber. Thus the problem of the broken track normally associated with spark chambers is eliminated.

Wire spark chambers provide a different advantage. Even though the use of spark chambers can cut down considerably on the number of photos taken for an experiment, we shall see later that scanning the photos and figuring out what happened is still quite a problem. The recent development of wire spark chambers has made it possible to do away with the photographic phase altogether, and to use electronic methods instead to record the track of a particle.

Several different ways of accomplishing this have been devised. One is called the sparkostrictive wire chamber. The figure shows the wire planes that form the heart of the chamber being "wound". These wire planes take the place of the plates used in the original spark chamber. In use, these planes are placed parallel to each other, but with the wires in one plane at right angles to the adjacent one. In a manner similar to the spark chamber operation described earlier, a voltage is maintained between the planes. Thus when a particle enters the chamber a spark jumps between two of the wires.

Here is where the big difference arises. No photo is taken. Instead the spark causes an acoustic (or sound) pulse to flow along the wires. Again, there are a number of ways to utilize this pulse; but basically the time it takes for the pulse to reach a sensor in each direction (left-right and up-down) is measured. Since we know the velocity of sound in the wire, it is easy to calculate (automatically) the location of the particle on that plane. This is shown schematically in the figure, and it is exactly like locating a point on a two-dimensional graph. Particles can be located to an accuracy of .01 millimeter in this way. As in a standard spark chamber, a series of these planes is required to provide a three-dimensional record of the track.

Thus we have a filmless spark chamber. But the required information, rather than being stored on photographic film, is now in the form of a series of pairs of coordinates that are easily stored in a computer. We shall see later that this technique has turned out to be extraordinarily useful.

The figure shows the use of wire spark chambers, Čerenkov counters, and bending magnets in a complex coincidence circuit.

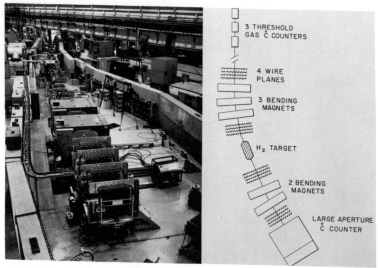

Wire spark chambers, Čerenkov counters, and bending magnets (to help separate wanted from unwanted particles) used in a complex coincidence circuit. Drawing at right shows arrangement of equipment.

Nuclear Photographic Emulsions

In 1896 the French physicist Henri Becquerel discovered radioactivity. The detection device he used was a photographic plate.

Although the photographic method was used sporadically in nuclear physics studies over the next four decades or so, it was pushed into the background by the development of the various other detection devices we have discussed. One of the problems with the use of photographic plates was the fact that the emulsion was so thin.

As a result only those reactions that spread out within the plane of the emulsion itself were recorded. Otherwise the technique could be used to record little more than the fact that an event had occurred. But even this can be useful. Employees working in a radiation environment often wear a film badge—a small square of film wrapped in black paper. Development of the badge shows the amount of radiation to which the worker has been exposed.

Thanks to the development of special *nuclear photographic emulsions* in the 1940s, there was a revival of interest in the nuclear emulsion technique for experimental purposes. It has since been widely applied in cosmic-ray physics and was used in the discovery of both pi- and K-mesons. Emulsions are now available that are particularly sensitive to certain types of radiation.

In order to do more than just record the arrival of particles, however, the emulsion on the plates must be thick enough to provide a third dimension. Nuclear emulsions more than a sixteenth of an inch thick have been used, but require special developing techniques. Whereas ordinary film requires well under an hour for processing, a thick nuclear emulsion may take 2 weeks!

Because of the high density of the material (which may be 80% silver bromide), incoming particles are stopped in a far shorter distance than in cloud or bubble chambers, and the sixteenth of an inch thickness may be enough, especially if the particle is moving at an angle through the emulsion.

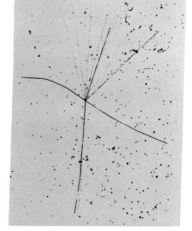

A high-energy, heavy, cosmic-ray particle often produces a cascade of particle tracks when it smashes into the grains in a nuclear emulsion plate.

The silver grains, though much finer than in ordinary film, will be similarly "exposed" when hit by a particle. After development, the grains form a track similar to, but much shorter than, a bubble chamber track. An alpha particle from a radioactive source will travel only a few thousandths of an inch in the emulsion. The track is normally examined with a special binocular microscope. Alternatively, it can be blown up photographically as in the figure on page 39. Under high magnification, particle tracks can be measured down to thousandths of a millimeter.

For high energies and long track lengths, the thickness of a single plate may not be sufficient. In this case a special type of film, which has no glass backing, is used so that many can be stacked together without "blank" spaces between them. The sheets of emulsion, called *pellicles,* are stacked as shown in the figure. As many as 200 or 300 pellicles may be used to provide the necessary depth. The emulsions are separated

Nuclear emulsion stack consisting of 240 sheets of emulsion produces results in three dimensions. Size is indicated by architect's scale at bottom of photo.

before development and later recombined. These emulsion stacks are especially useful where a portable detector is required, as in a rocket-launched, cosmic-ray experiment.

Plastic Detectors

A variation on this technique has recently been developed. A charged particle moving through certain solid substances leaves an actual path of damaged material a few atoms in diameter instead of a developable image. If the material is then chemically etched by submerging it in an acid, as shown in the figure on page 42, the track is enlarged until it can be seen with an ordinary light microscope or even by the naked eye.

Although any electrically insulating material, such as glass or mica, can be used as the detector, a special plastic called Lexan has been developed for use in cosmic-ray work. As with standard nuclear emulsions, these are in sheet form and can be used in stacks. The figure shows the formation of a cosmic-ray track. The etched portions are conical in shape because the acid solution starts attacking the surface and works its way in. Thus the portion of the track nearest the surface is exposed longest. Note too that the track gets thicker toward the end of the track as the particle slows down.

As in other track-forming techniques, this one utilizes the length, position, and thickness of the track for analysis (e.g., to determine the atomic number of the element involved). However, there is a major, and very valuable, difference. Standard cosmic-ray detectors, such as electronic counters and nuclear emulsions, work more efficiently with light cosmic rays, such as hydrogen and helium nuclei, than with heavy ones such as iron. In contrast, the new etched-track detector has a resolution that increases as the size of the incident nucleus goes up. Scientists have therefore been able to identify, for the first time, the nuclei of individual atomic particles that are heavier than silicon in low-energy cosmic rays.

One surprising result has been a report from the General Electric Research Center in Schenectady, New York, that iron and a neighboring element in the periodic table seem to be present in about equal amounts. This contradicts what would be expected if the idea held by some scientists is true—namely that the origin of cosmic rays lies in supernovas.* According to this theory, the most abundant heavy element among cosmic rays should be iron, the most stable of the elements. If manganese nuclei are as common as iron nuclei in the incoming radiation, scientists will have to either revamp their ideas regarding a connection between

---

*A supernova is the explosion of a star. The resulting light is sometimes 100 million times greater than that of our sun.

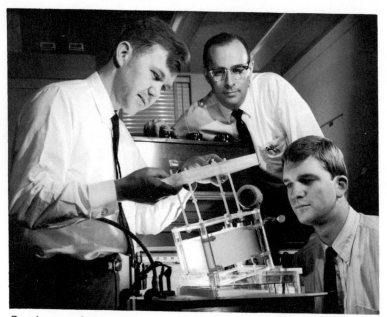

Developers of the Lexan track detector (left to right), Dr. P. Buford Price, Dr. Robert L. Fleischer, and David D. Peterson, prepare to lower plastic sheets into etching solution. This will enlarge cosmic-ray tracks so that they are visible to the naked eye.

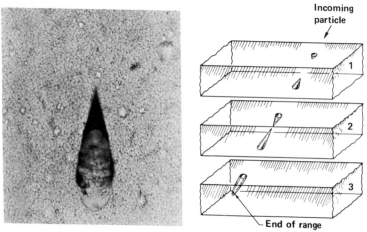

Formation of cosmic-ray track in plastic detector. Etched portions are conical because etching solution starts attacking the surface and works its way in.

exploding stars and cosmic rays, or else drop the idea altogether as a possible cause.

Track etching is finding use in a number of fields, including biology, anthropology, paleontology (the study of fossilized animals and plants), and astronomy. Meteorites, for example, are old (in the range of 4½ billion years) and have had long exposure to cosmic rays (from a million to a billion years). Clearly, they must contain a wealth of information about the early history of the solar system as well as about cosmic radiation. Thanks to the "fossil" tracks left by both cosmic rays and spontaneously fissioning atoms, these mineral treasure houses are being made to "talk".

Another intriguing application is the study of such fossil tracks in lunar material. These should tell us the rate of erosion of the lunar surface, when the moon solidified, and many other important facts about that body.

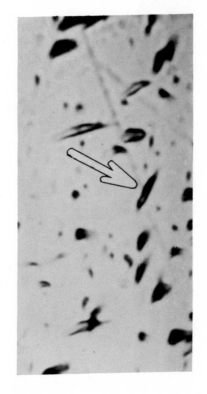

By etching fragments of lunar material collected by the Apollo-11 astronauts, scientists have discovered that the rocks are riddled with tracks left by cosmic rays. Studies of the tracks may provide clues to the origin of cosmic rays. Arrow points to a typical cosmic-ray track.

COMPUTERS ENTER THE SCENE

Probably the most important development in nuclear and high-energy physics has been the particle accelerator. In its various shapes and sizes it has been a major tool for the experimenter. The theoretical physicist, for example, has been hard put to explain and classify the several hundred elementary particles that have been found over the last decade or so.

In the detector field, the bubble chamber has been the most useful tool in high-energy physics, while the semiconductor detector has had the greatest impact in the nuclear or low-energy area. Since the semiconductor devices are compact and easily arranged in arrays, scientists have been able to accumulate data in nuclear experiments at a rapid rate. This, as you may recognize, has its bad as well as its good points.

It leads us to another development that has had a great impact in these fields; yet it is a development that you probably would not even recognize as a tool of nuclear scientists. This is the computer. Particle physics experiments often produce mountains of data that must be sorted and analyzed. When bubble chambers are used, one experiment may produce hundreds of thousands of photographs.

The point here is that many of the most successful experiments could never even have been contemplated were it not for the availability of large high-speed computers.

Bubble chamber pictures, for example, must be examined one by one. Even if done by a skilled operator, it might take half a minute to decide whether the picture contains something of interest. If so, careful measurements must be made, particles identified, momenta calculated, and so on. The process, illustrated in the figure at the top of page 45, is both difficult and tedious.

One of the first successful attempts to break the logjam of bubble chamber pictures was a machine devised by James Franck (and eventually nicknamed the "Franckenstein"). Originally designed for use with the 72-inch bubble chamber at the Lawrence Radiation Laboratory in Berkeley,

Scanning bubble chamber film.

California, it automatically enters the coordinates of an event or interaction into a computer, which then does the necessary calculations. That is, the computer reconstructs and analyzes the event.

However, while this eliminates much tedious "pencil work", each of the particle paths must still be picked out and tracked manually. An operator is shown doing this on a similar machine, the Scanning Measurement Projector, below.

Semiautomatic Scanning Measurement Projector at the Lawrence Radiation Laboratory. As the operator tracks the particle paths manually, measurements are automatically sent to a computer for immediate analysis.

The ultimate objective of course was equipment that could do the entire job automatically. An important step along the way was, and is, the Spiral Reader, a semiautomatic device developed at Lawrence Radiation Laboratory. Its major advantage over earlier readers is that once the device is manually "locked" onto the vertex of the event being analyzed, it will scan the rest of the picture itself. The scan starts at the vertex and moves out in an ever-widening spiral,

The Spiral Reader, a semiautomatic device, can "read" as many as 100 bubble chamber events per hour.

with only a little help required now and then from the operator. This device can "read" as many as 100 bubble chamber events per hour—10 times as many as older devices.

And, finally, a device has been developed that actually will do the entire job automatically (although thus far it has not proved to be much of a time-saver). The Flying Spot Digitizer was put into service in 1965 at the Brookhaven National Laboratory in Upton, New York. In this system, a spot of light moves back and forth across the film, rather like the electron beam of a television set, and the variations in light output are received by a photomultiplier behind the

Flying Spot Digitizer provides completely automatic analysis of particle tracks in bubble chamber film, which is seen entering the system at lower right.

film. These variations, which are representative of particle position, type, energy, etc., are converted to digital signals for processing by a larger computer.

An example of what can be done is shown in the figure on page 47. This pair of photos comes from equipment under development at Yale University and the Massachusetts Institute of Technology. The equipment is called PEPR

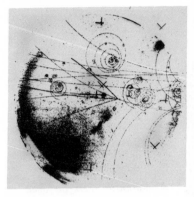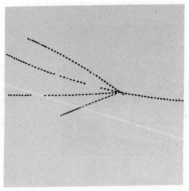

The desired set of particle tracks (right) has been automatically picked out of the background clutter in the actual bubble chamber photo (left).

(*P*recision *E*ncoding and *P*attern *R*ecognition). The bubble chamber photograph is shown in (a), while the desired set of tracks, picked out of the background clutter, is shown in (b). The computer is programmed to "try out" various possible particle interactions that might explain the particle tracks and choose the proper one.

But, remarkable as these operations may be, they are still "after-the-fact" analysis. The problem is that time on the big accelerators is hard to get; after you have made your runs, you can't wait for results to see whether everything is all right, or whether you should have made some adjustments or variations in your experiment. When you complete the data taking, you pack up and get out. Often, however, later analysis of the data reveals information that would have been extremely useful had it been available while you were running your experiment. In such case, your only alternative is to use the data as is or go back on the waiting list.

Today, thanks to a process called *on-line computing*, this is a problem that appears less often. For the computers can now be an actual part of the experiment and can process a sampling of the data as the experiment is being run. In this way the experimenter knows immediately whether his equipment is working properly, and indeed whether his entire experiment has been designed properly. The filmless spark

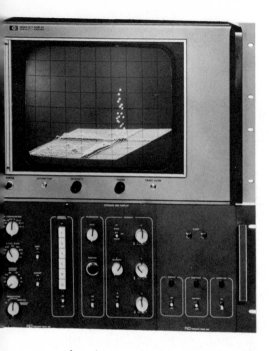

A computer can be used to combine counts from two or more detectors, while a cathode-ray tube can display results in a vast variety of ways. Result shown here is an isometric display of a two-detector coincidence experiment.

chambers, which we mentioned earlier, provide natural partners to the computer since their results are by their very nature machine processable.

The figure above shows another way that the computer has become useful. Here we see how the computer can take information from a pair of detectors and combine them immediately into a three-dimensional display, called a "contour display".

An important type of detection device that has come into service along with the computer is the *hodoscope*. The term derives from the Greek, *hodos*, which means path or track, and is used to describe a device that combines counters in such a way that a good indication of particle position is given. For example, in some high-energy physics experiments, the rate of data accumulation exceeds even the capacity of a spark chamber.

In this case the *scintillation detector hodoscope* is used. The "marriage" of detection equipment and computer is clearly shown. The hodoscope is at the left; it consists of an array of vertical scintillator strips, which count the number

Data from hodoscope at left is entered directly into data center trailer at right. Computer in trailer is "on line" performing analysis as the experiment is conducted.

of times each vertical section has been struck by a forward-scattered, high-energy particle emerging from the chamber at the far left.

The trailer at the right is a 40-foot mobile computer facility used at Brookhaven National Laboratory. Designed for particle research, it can service several experiments simultaneously and accepts inputs from as many as 128 detection devices. Its mobility means that it can be moved to various parts of the large target building as the need arises.

Continued development of detectors and computers promises great advances in industry, science, and medicine, and in that most basic science of all, the study of matter.

SUGGESTED REFERENCES

Books

Cosmic Rays, Bruno Rossi, McGraw-Hill Book Company, New York, 1964, 268 pp., $7.00 (hardback); $2.95 (paperback).

Elementary Particles, David H. Frish and Alan M. Thorndike, Van Nostrand Reinhold Company, New York 1964, 153 pp., $1.75.

Elementary Particles: A Short History of Some Discoveries in Atomic Physics, Chen Ning Yang, Princeton University Press, Princeton, New Jersey, 1961, 65 pp., $3.50.

The Fundamental Particles, Clifford E. Swartz, Addison-Wesley Publishing Company, Inc., Reading, Massachusetts, 1965, 152 pp., $3.95 (hardback); $2.95 (paperback).

High Energy Physics, Hal Hellman, J. B. Lippincott Company, Philadelphia, Pennsylvania, 1968, 192 pp., $4.75.

Inside the Atom (revised edition), Isaac Asimov, Abelard-Schuman, Ltd., New York, 1966, 197 pp., $4.00.

Inside the Nucleus, Irving Adler, The John Day Company, Inc., New York, 1963, 192 pp., $4.95 (hardback); $0.60 (paperback) from the New American Library, Inc., New York.

The New Age in Physics (second edition), Sir Harrie Massey, Basic Books, Inc., New York, 1967, 386 pp., $10.00. (Detecting Fast Particles, pages 170-182.)

The Neutrino: Ghost Particle of the Atom, Isaac Asimov, Doubleday and Company, Inc., New York, 1966, 223 pp., $4.95 (hardback); $1.95 (paperback) from Dell Publishing Company, Inc., New York

Nuclear Physics and the Fundamental Particles, H. H. Heckman and P. W. Starring, Holt, Rinehart and Winston, New York, 1963, 410 pp., $2.60. (Out of print but available through libraries.)

Sourcebook on Atomic Energy (third edition), Samuel Glasstone, Van Nostrand Reinhold Company, New York, 1967, 883 pp., $9.25. Chapter 7, Detection and Measurement of Nuclear Radiation, pages 198-289.

The World of the Atom, 2 volumes, Henry A. Boorse and Lloyd Matz (Eds.) Basic Books, Inc., New York, 1966, 1873 pp., $35.00. Chapter 42, The Cloud Chamber, pages 676-689.

The World of Elementary Particles, Kenneth W. Ford, Blaisdell Publishing Company, Waltham, Massachusetts, 1963, 262 pp., $2.95.

Articles

Advances in Superconducting Magnets, W. B. Sampson, P. P. Craig, and M. Strongin, *Scientific American,* **216:** 114 (March 1967).

Detecting Nuclear Particles, *Science News,* **92:** 333 (September 30, 1967).

Neutrinos from the Atmosphere and Beyond, Frederick Reines and J. P. F. Sellschop, *Scientific American,* **214:** 40 (February 1966).

Nuclear Tracks in Solids, R. L. Fleischer, et. al., *Scientific American,* **220:** 30 (June 1969).

The Omega-Minus Experiment, W. B. Fowler and N. P. Samios, *Scientific American,* **211:** 36 (October 1964).

Semiconductor Particle Detectors, O. M. Bilaniuk, *Scientific American,* **207:** 78 (October 1962).

The Spark Chamber, G. K. O'Neill, *Scientific American,* **207**: 36 (August 1962).

The Streamer Chamber, D. E. Yount, *Scientific American,* **217**: 38 (October 1967).

The Two-Neutrino Experiment, Leon Lederman, *Scientific American,* **208**: 60 (March 1963).

Motion Pictures

Available for loan without charge from the AEC Headquarters Film Library, Division of Public Information, U. S. Atomic Energy Commission, Washington, D. C. 20545 and from other AEC film libraries.

Exploring the Atomic Nucleus, $13\frac{1}{2}$ minutes, color, 1969. This film shows some recent discoveries made by physicists, the basic equipment they used, and how they analyzed the resulting data. New atomic particles, resulting from collisions of particles caused by accelerators, are directed into detection devices, such as scintillation counters, Čerenkov counters, spark chambers, and bubble chambers. Analysis of these particles and their interactions enables scientists to learn more about the basic nature of matter.

The High Energy People, $5\frac{1}{4}$ minutes, color, 1963. Scientists describe their work with the Zero Gradient Synchrotron and the Spark Chamber at the Argonne National Laboratory. The automatic cameras, which photograph the particle tracks, are explained as is the examination and analysis of the photographs.

Microscope for the Unknown, 29 minutes, black and white, 1965. Different types of experimental apparatus used in high-energy physics are illustrated at the Zero Gradient Synchrotron at the Argonne National Laboratory. Principles of track detectors, such as the bubble chamber and the spark chamber, are described, and the interpretation of track photographs is explained. A large spark chamber facility for detecting neutrinos and the 30-inch MURA bubble chamber are illustrated in detail.

Of Man and Matter, 29 minutes, color, 1963. The operation and components of the Alternating Gradient Synchrotron at the Brookhaven National Laboratory are described. An actual experiment is shown in which the particle beam is guided into a bubble chamber and the resultant interactions with the target nuclei are photographed. The methods used in scanning and analyzing the photographs are also explained.

Radiation Detection by Ionization, 30 minutes, black and white, 1962. Basic principles of ionization detectors are described. Ionization chambers, proportional counters, and Geiger counters are explained and shown in operation. Special attention is given to Geiger counters. The resolving time of a counter is also discussed.

Radiation Detection by Scintillation, 30 minutes, black and white, 1962. The scintillation process is described, and the efficiency of the conversion of gamma radiation to visible light in the scintillator is discussed. Solid and liquid scintillators are shown along with special detection devices using this principle. A description of the operation of a photomultiplier tube is given, and the concept of pulse height is developed. The principle of operation of a pulse-height analyzer is shown, and the spectrum obtained with such an instrument is discussed.

APPENDIX

How to Build a Simple Diffusion Cloud Chamber

1. Select a jar with a tight cover, such as a peanut butter jar or a transparent plastic refrigerator jar. (It will be necessary to seal the jar so that it is leak-proof against an air pressure the equivalent of several millimeters of mercury.)

2. Cut a piece of black blotter paper or felt about 2 inches wide and long enough to fit around the inside of the jar near the bottom and glue it in place. Use rubber base glue and allow glue to dry completely. Unless it dries thoroughly, the solvent in the glue will prevent operation of the cloud chamber.

3. Paint the inside of the jar's cover with flat black paint and allow the paint to dry.

4. In the bottom of the jar, glue a piece of felt or blotter paper cut in doughnut shape using the same glue as in (2). (See Figure 1.)

5. Saturate the blotter paper or felt with alcohol (any kind—isopropyl rubbing compound, ethyl, methyl, etc.).

6. Put cover in place and seal tightly.

7. Invert the jar so that the metal cap is on the bottom and place on a cake of dry ice (solid CO_2).

8. Direct an intense, well-focussed light beam at the jar as in Figure 2. (An ordinary light source is too weak.) Light from a microscope or a high-intensity lamp works well. (A flashlight can be used successfully if the beam is intense enough and sufficiently well focussed.) The light beam should be no more than 1 inch to $1\frac{1}{4}$ inches in diameter.

9. Examine the fog that should be falling like rain. Near the bottom, which should be near the temperature of dry ice ($-77°C$), short tracks should form.

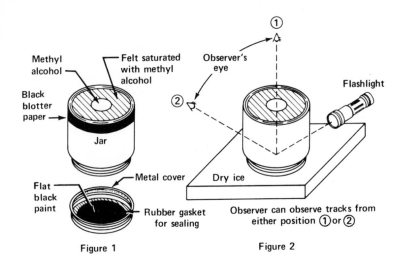

Methyl alcohol

Felt saturated with methyl alcohol

Observer's eye

Black blotter paper

Flashlight

Jar

Metal cover

Dry ice

Flat black paint

Rubber gasket for sealing

Observer can observe tracks from either position ① or ②

Figure 1

Figure 2

Possible Reasons for Failure

1. If the chamber fails to show any rain or precipitation, either the bottom is not cold enough, or there is not enough alcohol.

2. If there is steady rain but no tracks, look for a leak in the jar. Outside air may be leaking in and contaminating the cloud chamber. If there is no air leak, and there is only a steady fall of rain, perhaps there is chemical contamination from either the felt or glue. To correct this, one usually has to start over, although sometimes the condition can be eliminated by airing the jar for a day.

THE AUTHOR

HAL HELLMAN is a free-lance science writer. Although he writes for both specialists and the nontechnical public (including young adults), he prefers to interpret science for the latter, believing that it is both more difficult and more rewarding. The titles of his books reflect a wide range of interests—*The Art and Science of Color; The City in the World of the Future; Communications in the World of the Future; Transportation in the World of the Future; Controlled Guidance Systems; Defense Mechanisms: From Virus to Man; Energy and Inertia; Inertia; High Energy Physics; Light and Electricity in the Atmosphere; Navigation: Land, Sea, and Sky; The Right Size: Why Some Creatures Survive and Others Are Extinct;* and *Lasers* and *Spectroscopy,* other booklets in this series.

Prior to going into full-time writing, Mr. Hellman was with General Precision, Inc. for 10 years. During his second five-year period he was Manager of Information Services, and it was during that time that his interest in science writing began.

Mr. Hellman holds a B.A. in Economics, an M.A. in Industrial Management, and an M.S. in Physics. He is a member of the National Association of Science Writers.

PHOTO CREDITS

Cover courtesy Dr. Erwin W. Mueller, The Pennsylvania State University

Page

1	University of Chicago
8	Union Carbide Corporation (left); Brookhaven National Laboratory (BNL)
12	Pilot Chemicals Division, New England Nuclear Corporation
14	BNL (left); Los Alamos Scientific Laboratory (right); General Electric/Hanford Plant (bottom).
15 & 16	Stanford University
17	From the May 1964 *Nucleonics.* Copyright © by McGraw-Hill Book Company, Inc. Redrawn by permission.
20	Lawrence Radiation Laboratory (LRL)
27	C. D. Anderson (left)
28	Johns Hopkins University Library (left); BNL
30	BNL
31	Argonne National Laboratory
33	BNL
35	Hal Hellman (right)
36	LRL
38 & 39	BNL
40	LRL
42 & 43	General Electric Research and Development Center
45	BNL (top); LRL
46	LRL (top); BNL
47	Irwin Ac Press (left)
48	Nuclear Data, Inc.
49-53	BNL

This booklet is one of the "Understanding the Atom" Series. Comments are invited on this booklet and others in the series; please send them to the Division of Technical Information, U. S. Atomic Energy Commission, Washington, D. C. 20545.

Published as part of the AEC's educational assistance program, the series includes these titles:

A single copy of any one booklet, or of no more than three different booklets, may be obtained free by writing to:

USAEC, P. O. BOX 62, OAK RIDGE, TENNESSEE   37830

Complete sets of the series are available to school and public librarians, and to teachers who can make them available for reference or for use by groups. Requests should be made on school or library letterheads and indicate the proposed use.

Students and teachers who need other material on specific aspects of nuclear science, or references to other reading material, may also write to the Oak Ridge address. Requests should state the topic of interest exactly, and the use intended.

In all requests, include "Zip Code" in return address.

Printed in the United States of America

USAEC Division of Technical Information Extension, Oak Ridge, Tennessee

U. S. ATOMIC ENERGY COMMISSION
Division of Technical Information